MW00658373

Practice Test for the Naglieri Nonverbal Ability Test®* (NNAT®*)

Level B

By Mercer Publishing

Practice Test for the Naglieri Nonverbal Ability Test®* (NNAT®*) Level B

A study aid to help your child get into a gifted program.

Mercer Publishing

* NNAT® and Naglieri Nonverbal Ability Test® are registered trademarks of Harcourt Assessment, Inc. which was not involved in the production of, and does not endorse, this practice test.

Printed in the United States of America.

INTRODUCTION

As a parent and educator, I understand how important it is to ensure your children are given the opportunites they deserve when it comes to their education. One of the greatest opportunities your child will have is entering the gifted program, if they can qualify for the program based on their test scores.

One of the tools for measuring a student's ability to enter the gifted program is the Naglieri Nonverbal Ability Test®* (NNAT®*) published by Harcourt Assessment, Inc. The NNAT®* is a culture-fair, nonverbal measure of reasoning and problem solving abilities. This test does not require English language skills or mathematics, instead consisting of problems that use a complex set of geometric shapes and designs. It is a 38 question test with four types of questions: Pattern Completion, Analogy, Serial Reasoning and Spatial Visualization. The number of questions in each test area varies by test level:

Level	Grade	Pattern Completion	Analogy	Serial Reasoning	Spatial Visualization	TOTAL
A	K	30	8			38
B	1	19	13	6		38
C	2	10	12	11	5	38
D	3 – 4	6	10	8	14	38
E	5 – 6	5	6	8	19	38
F	7 – 9	2	10	8	18	38
G	10 –12		7	7	24	38

Most resources state that there are really no ways to prepare for this test - that your child should only get a good night's sleep before taking the test. It is guaranteed that if your child has never done some of the types of problems before, that they will not do as well as they could on this test – perhaps jepordizing their admission into the gifted program. So what should the average parent do? If you have purchased this practice test, you have taken the first step.

This practice test, Practice Test for the Naglieri Nonverbal Ability Test®* (NNAT®*) - Level B, contains 38 questions in the three test areas found on the NNAT®* Level B, which is usually given to students in first grade:

Pattern Completion	19 questions
Reasoning by Analogy	13 questions
Serial Reasoning	6 questions

The object of this practice test is to familiarize your child with the types of questions they will face on test day, how the tests are formatted, and the number of questions in each test area. However, since this practice test has not been standardized with Harcourt Assessment and the actual NNAT®* test, a valid NNAT®* test score cannot be concluded from their results on this practice test.

Good luck on this practice test and your upcoming NNAT®* test.
Mercer Publishing

TABLE OF CONTENTS

TEST TAKING INFORMATION

The Naglieri Nonverbal Ability Test®* (NNAT®*) Level B, which is usually given to students in first grade is an untimed, multiple choice test.

The official guideline from the publisher is that students should not guess if they do not know the answer – that random guessing compromises the validity of the scores. However, the NNAT®* score is calculated based on the number of right answers and the student is not penalized for incorrect answers. As a parent looking for a high score, it is better for your child to answer all questions than leave an answer blank.

There are some approaches to standardized testing that have been proven to increase test scores. Review the following strategies with your child and have them practice these as they go through the practice test.

Listen Carefully. Instructions will be given to your child during the exam, including directions for each section and how to fill out the test forms. Many errors are made because children do not listen to the instructions as carefully as they should. If your child fills in the answers incorrectly or marks in the wrong section, your child's score will be lowered significantly.

Look at all the Available Answers. In their desire to finish quickly or first, many children select the first answer that seems right to them without looking all of the answers and choosing the one that best answers the question. No additional points are given for finishing the test early. Make sure your child understands the importance of evaluating all the answers before choosing one.

Skip Difficult Questions – Return to Them Later. Many children will sit and worry about a hard question, spending so much time on one problem that they never get to problems that they would be able to answer correctly if they only had enough time. Explain to your child that they can always return to a difficult question once they finish the test section.

Eliminate Answer Choices. If your child can eliminate one or more of the answer choices as definitely wrong, their chances of guessing correctly among the remaining choices improve their odds of getting the answer right.

Practice Filling Out a Bubble Test Form. Many errors are made on the NNAT®* exam because the students do not know how to fill out a bubble test form. A sample test form has been included in Appendix A. Have your child practice filling in answers in the bubbles in the sample form so they will know what to expect on the exam day.

Now, on to the practice test.

PATTERN COMPLETION

Each question in this section has a large rectangle with a picture or design. There is a small section of that picture hidden behind the rectangle with a question mark. The student should select the answer that best completes the picture.

Level B - 19 questions

1.

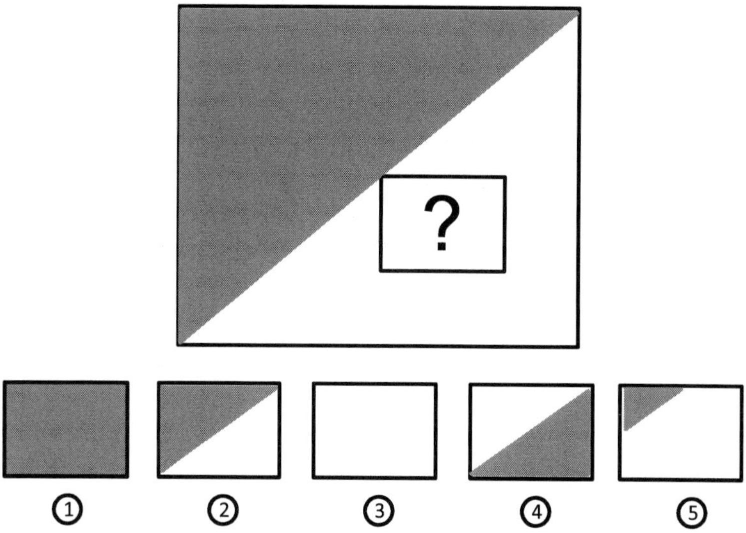

2.

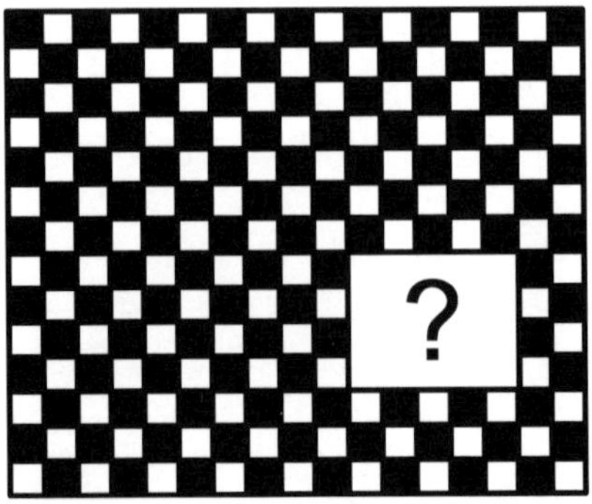

①　②　③　④　⑤

3.

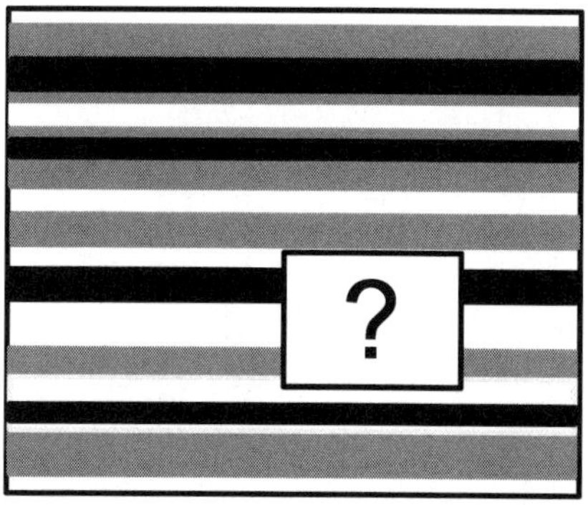

① ② ③ ④ ⑤

4.

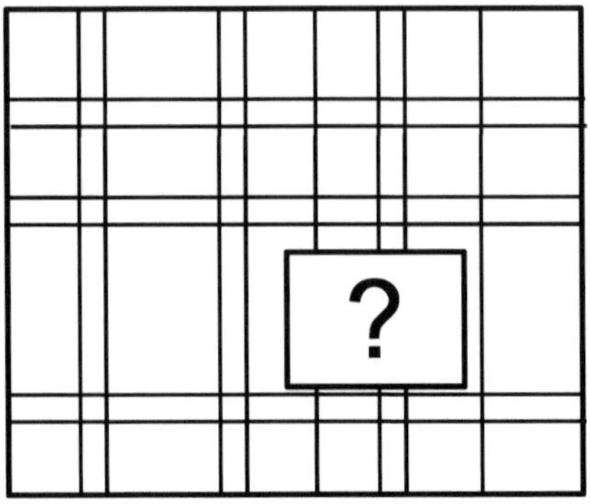

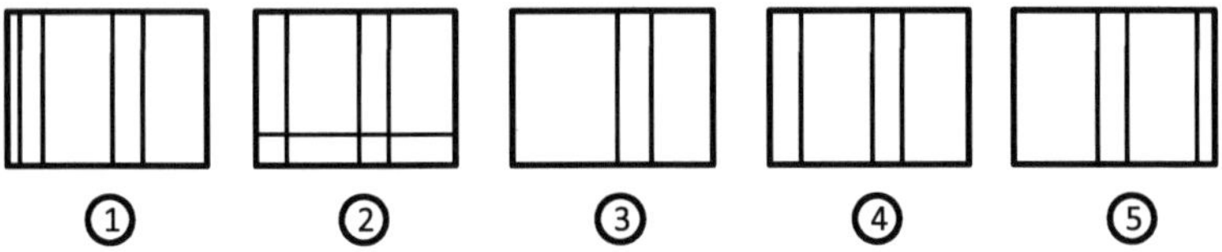

5.

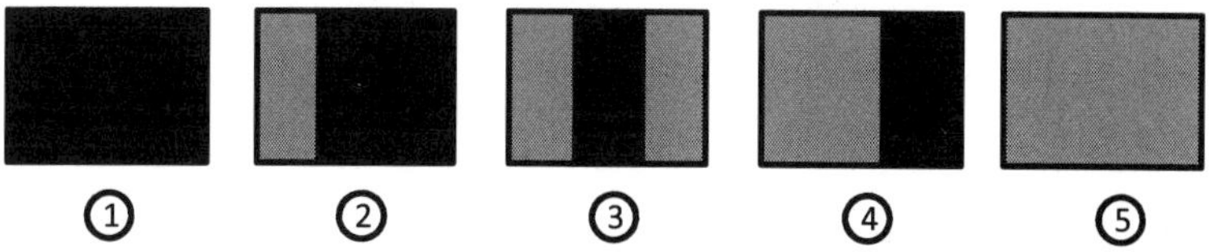

6.

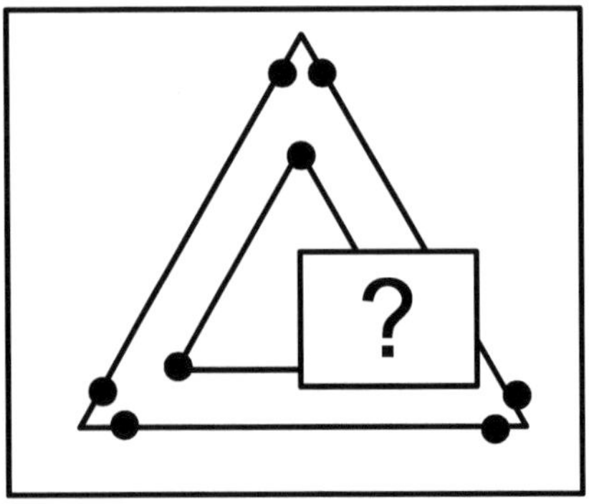

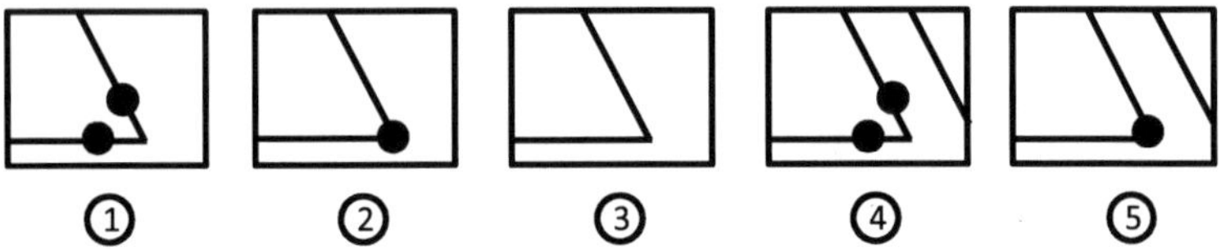

7.

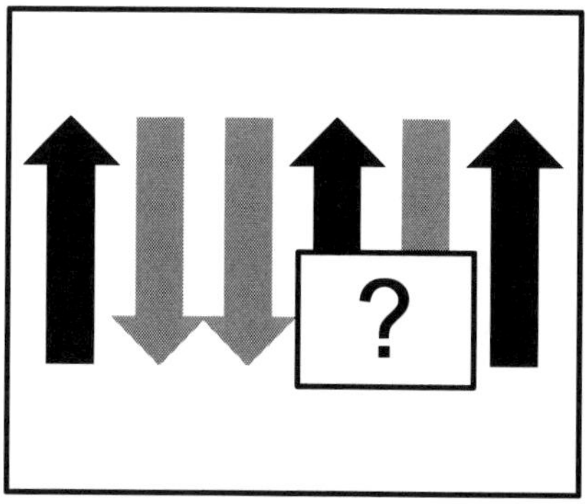

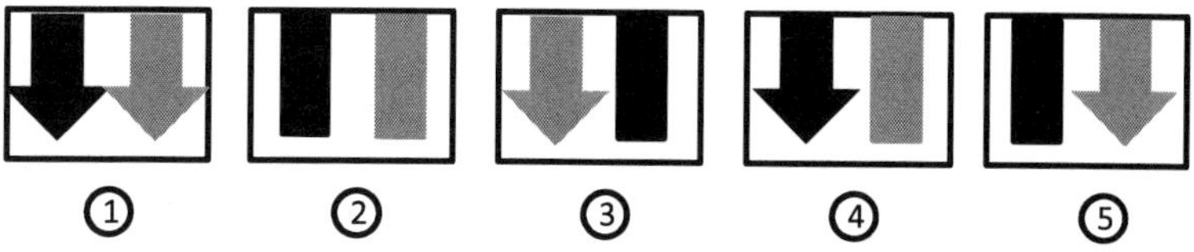

8.

① ② ③ ④ ⑤

9.

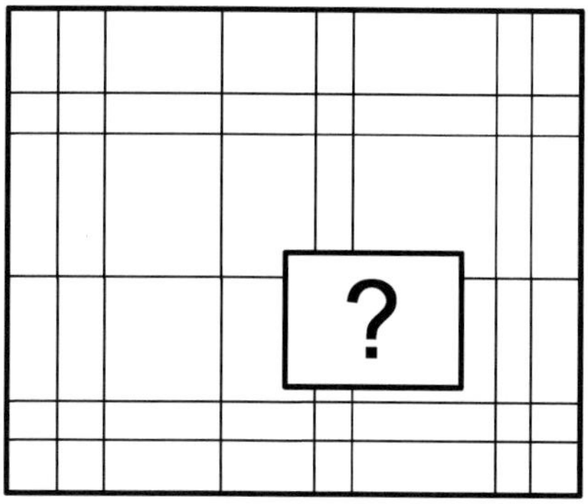

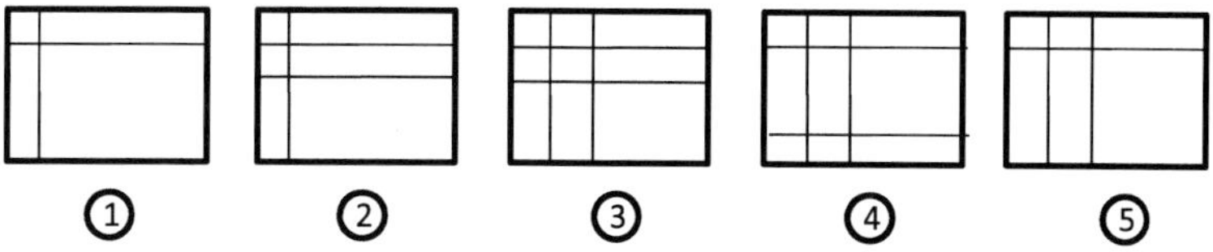

10.

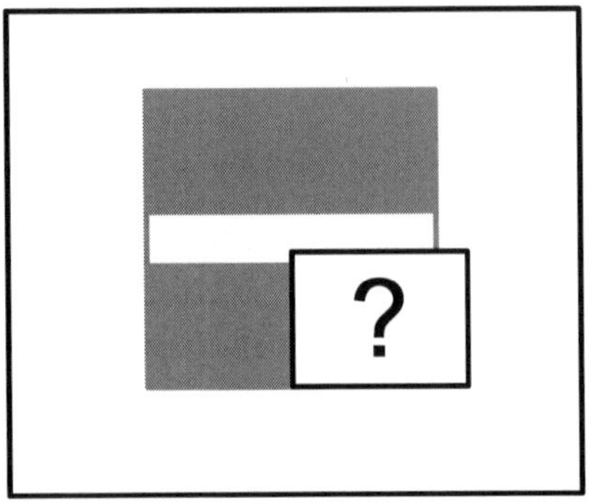

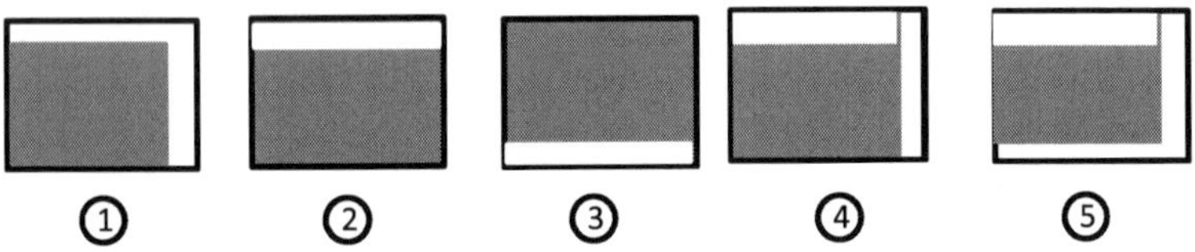

11.

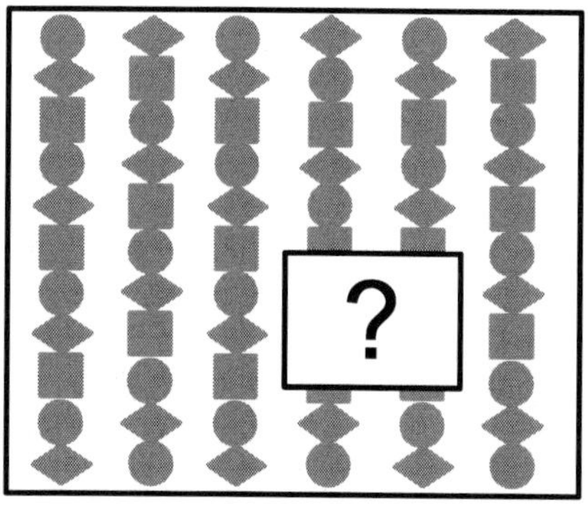

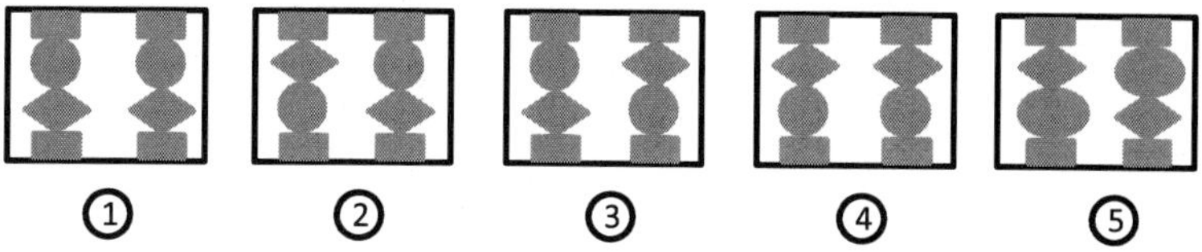

12.

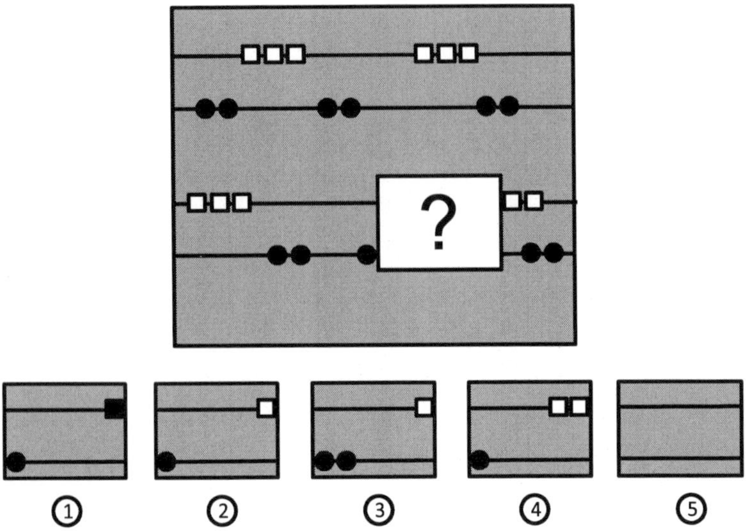

13.

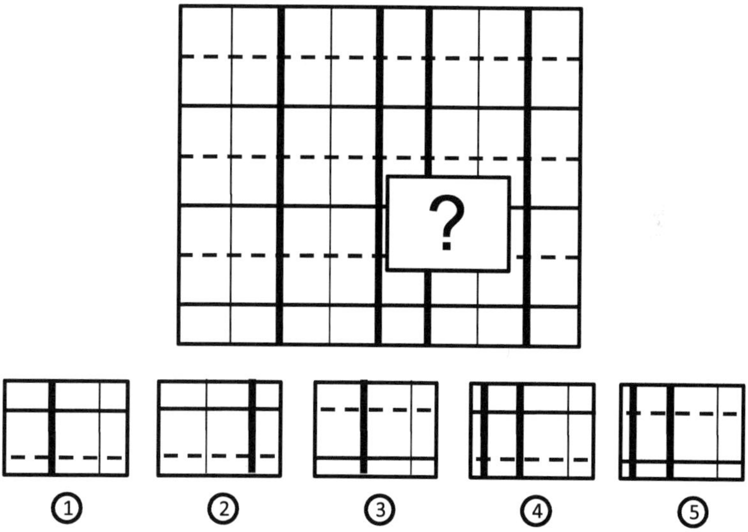

14.

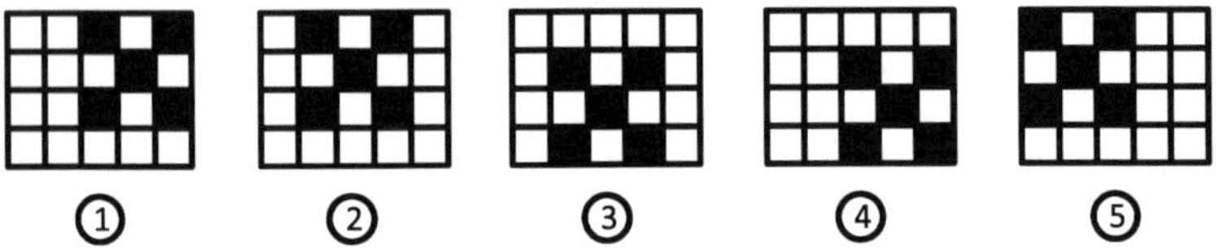

15.

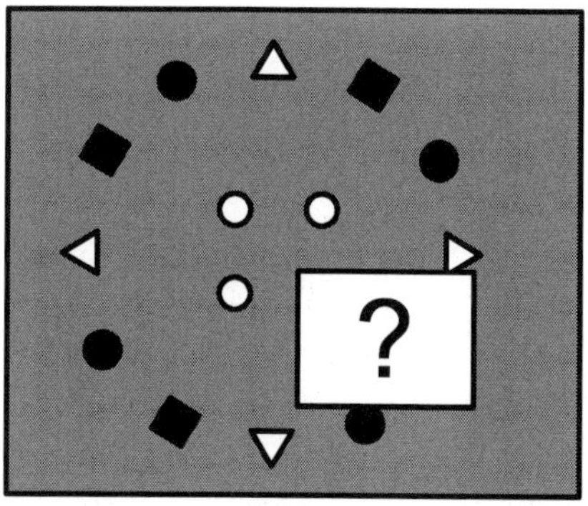

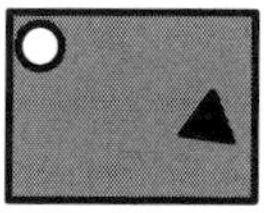

①

②

③

④

⑤

16.

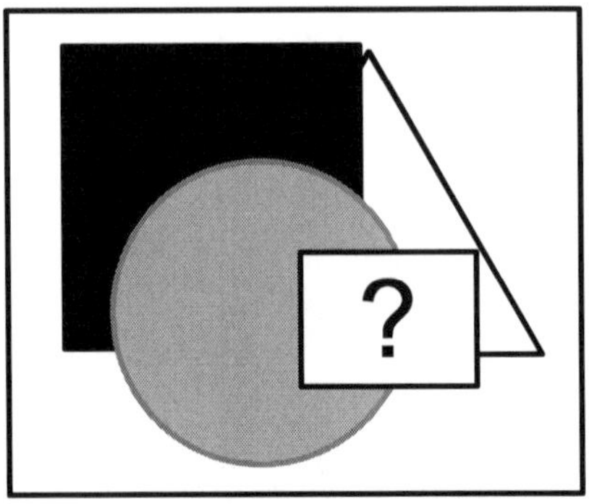

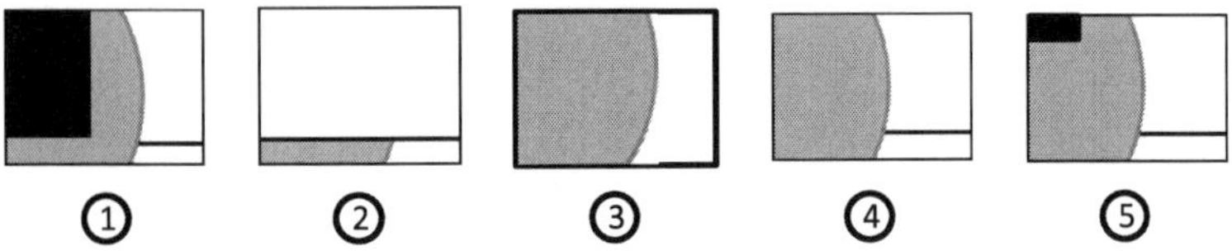

17.

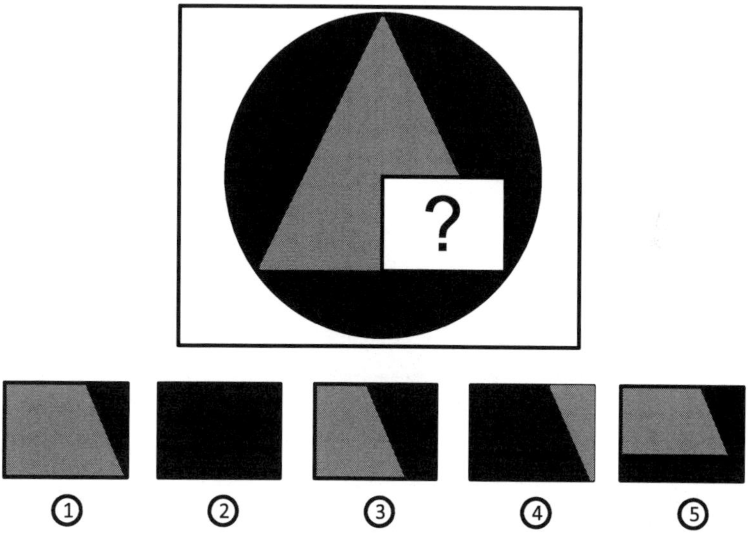

18.

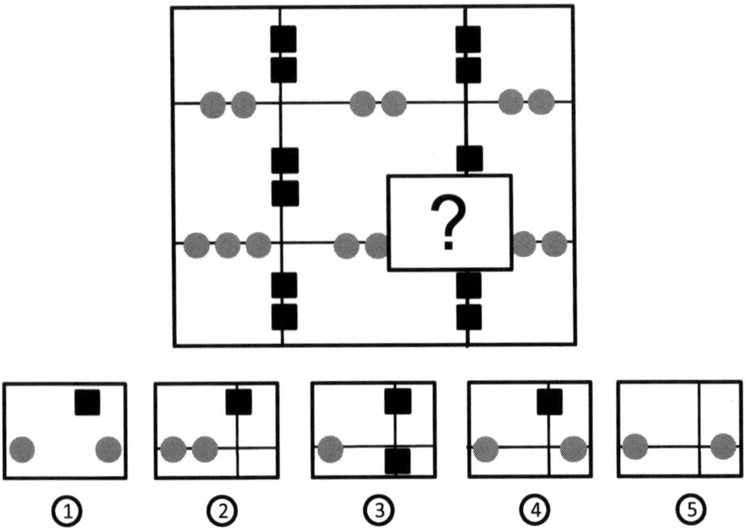

19.

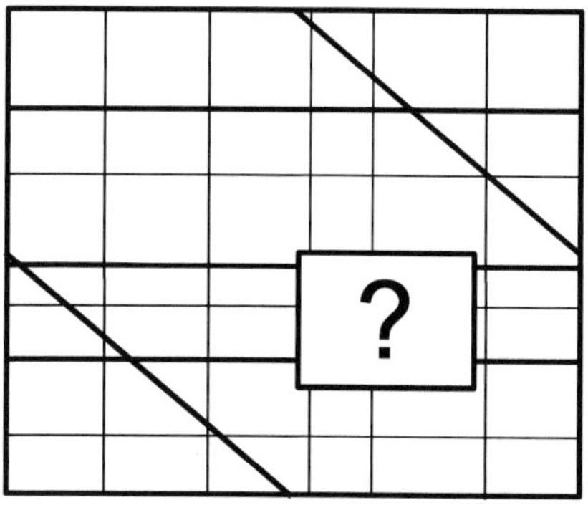

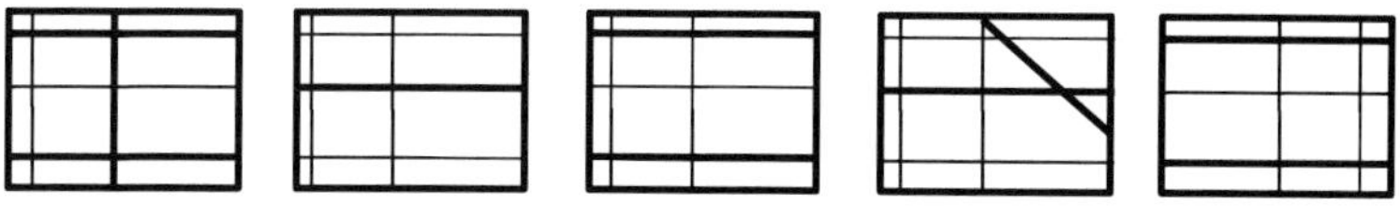

① ② ③ ④ ⑤

REASONING BY ANALOGY

In these questions the design of objects changes as the pictures go across the row. The student will need to determine how each of the objects is modified as they go from the first picture to the second picture in each row and, again, modified from the second picture to the third picture in, perhaps, a different way.

These same modifications should be reflected in the next rows. Select the figure from the five available answers that will be created when the same modifications are done to the third row of objects.

Level B - 13 questions

1.

① ② ③ ④ ⑤

2.

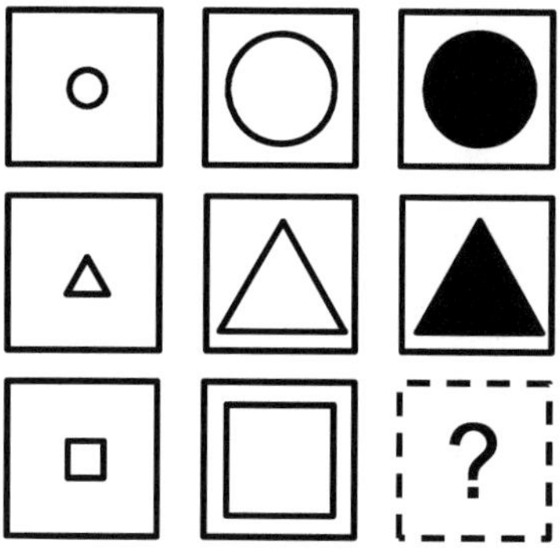

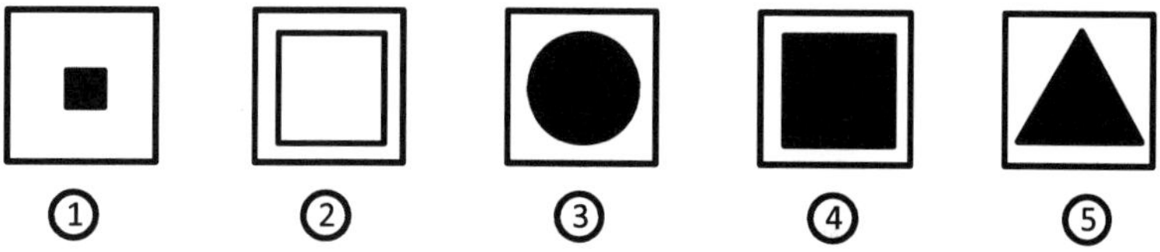

3.

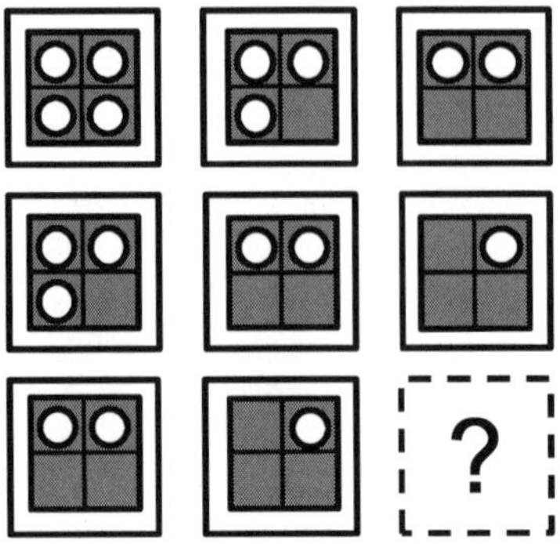

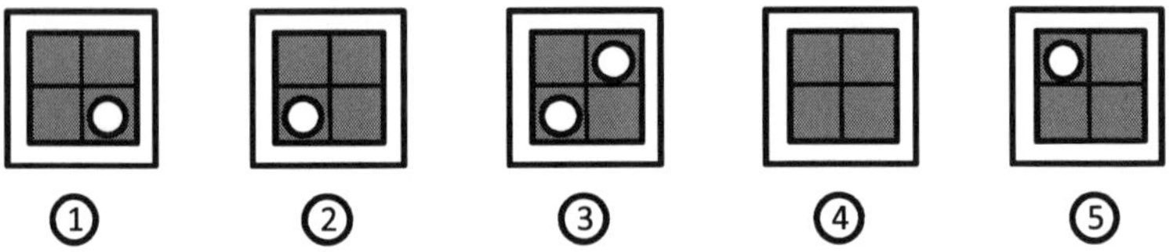

4.

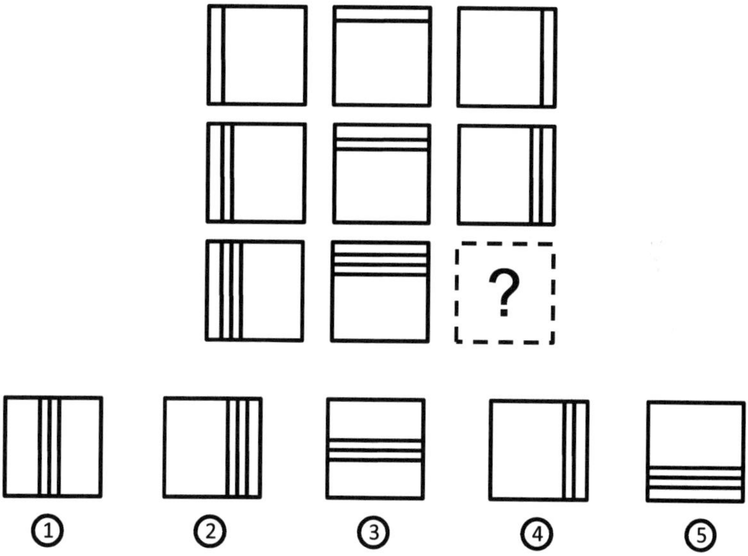

5.

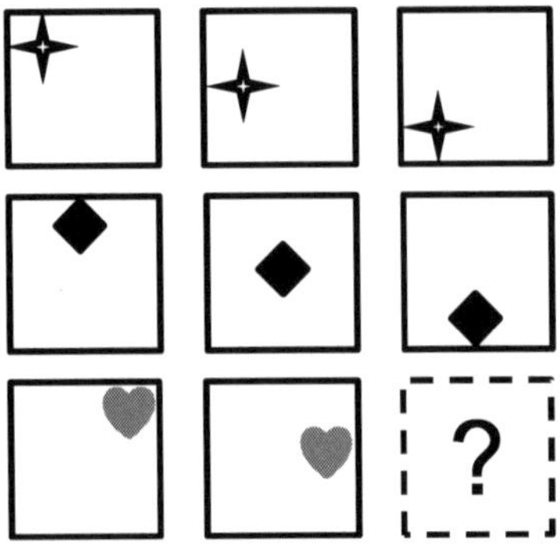

① ② ③ ④ ⑤

6.

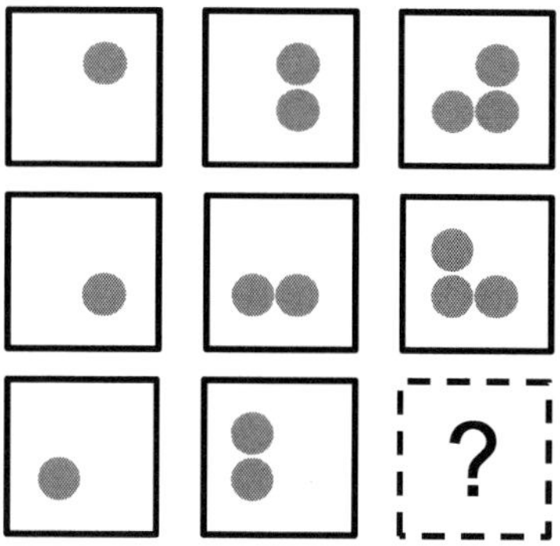

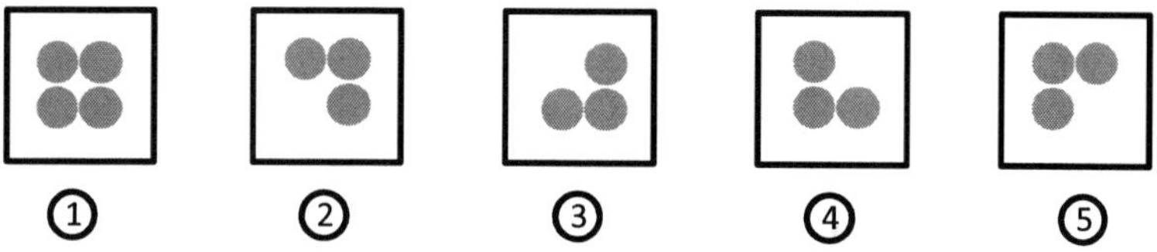

7.

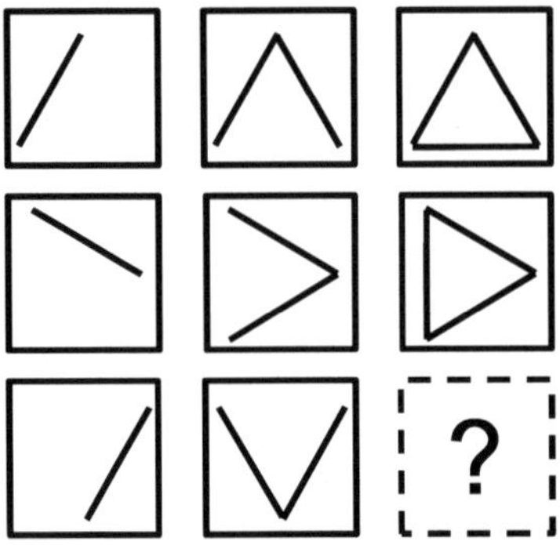

8.

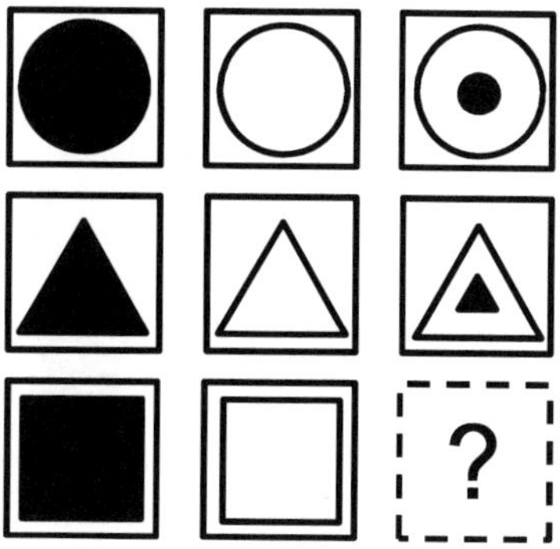

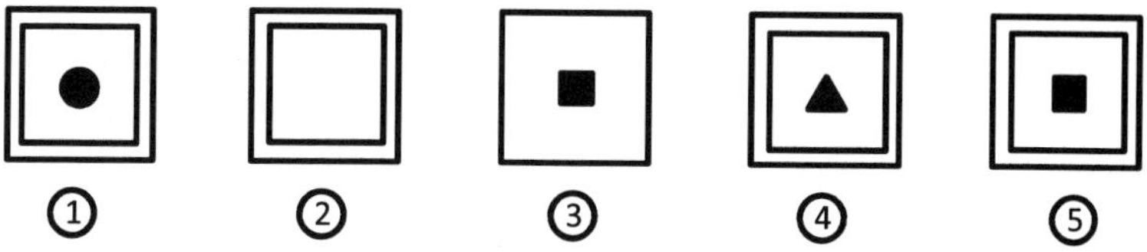

9.

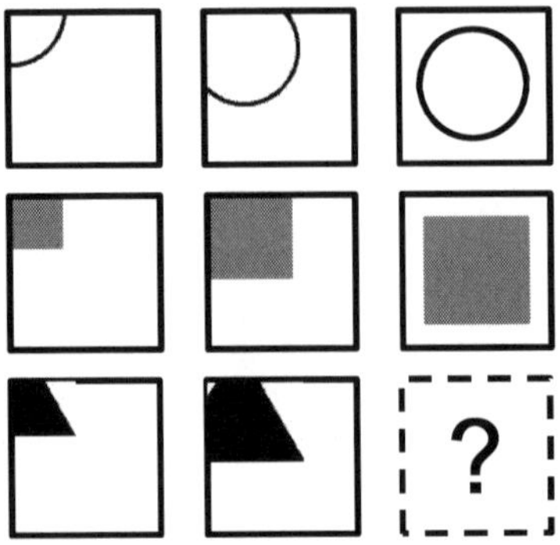

10.

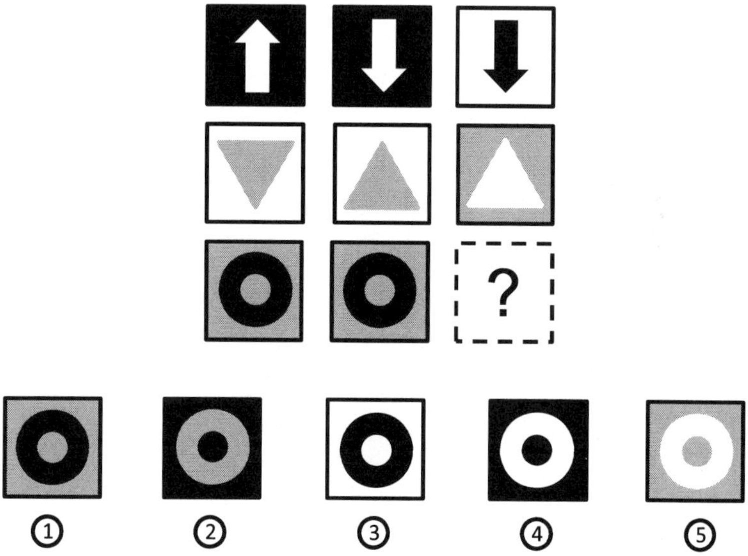

11.

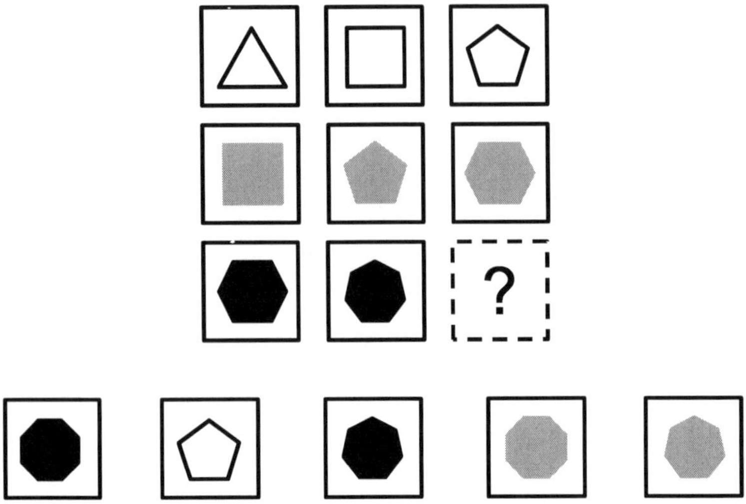

① ② ③ ④ ⑤

12.

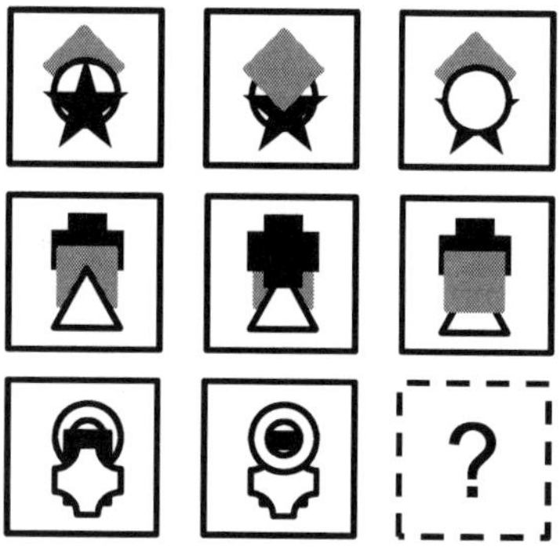

① ② ③ ④ ⑤

13.

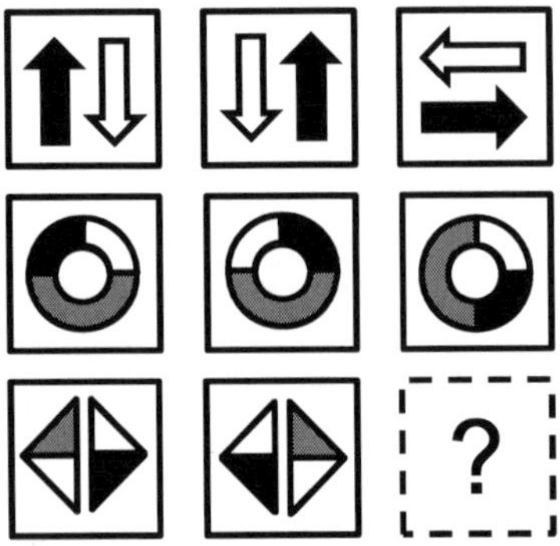

① ② ③ ④ ⑤

SERIAL REASONING

In these questions the design of objects changes as the pictures go across the row and down the columns. The student will need to determine sequences and patterns within the matrix and select the figure from the five available answers that will best complete the matrix.

Level B - 6 questions

1.

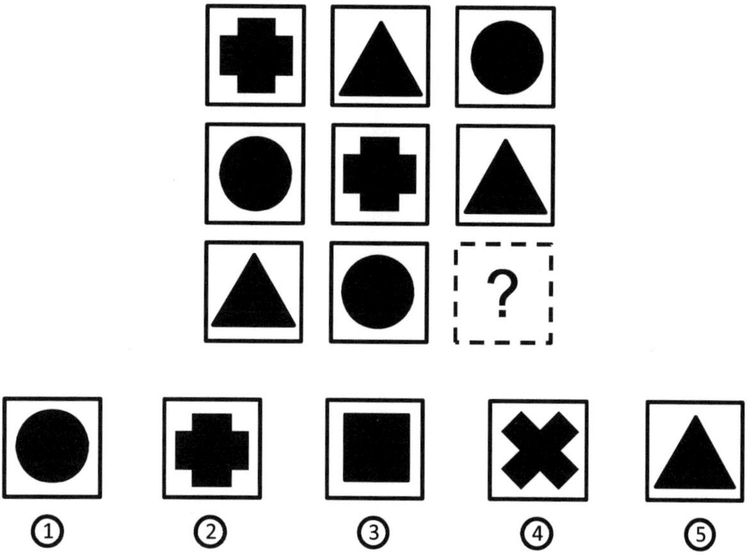

2.

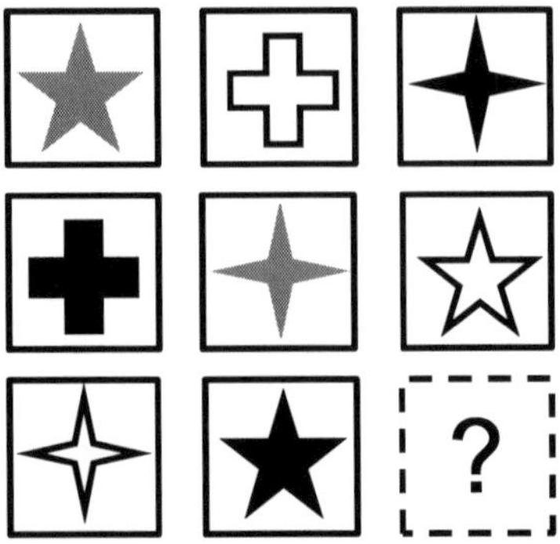

① ② ③ ④ ⑤

3.

① ② ③ ④ ⑤

4.

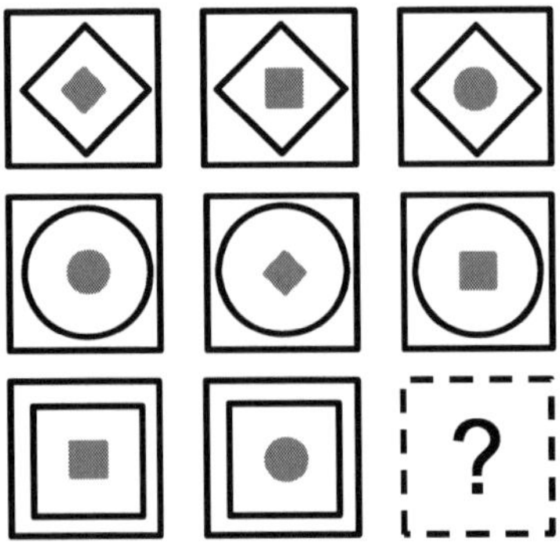

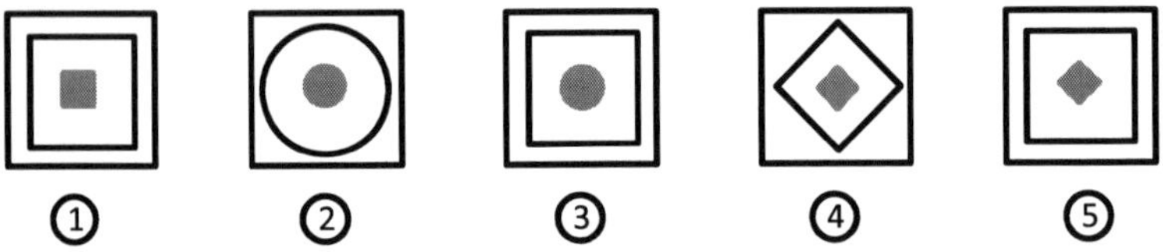

5.

6.

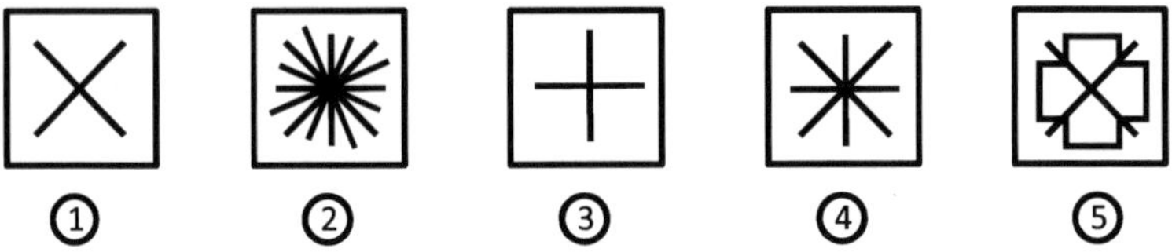

ANSWERS

PATTERN COMPLETION

1. 3
2. 4
3. 2
4. 4
5. 4
6. 5
7. 5
8. 2
9. 5
10. 4
11. 2
12. 2
13. 1
14. 4
15. 2
16. 4
17. 1
18. 4
19. 3

REASONING BY ANALOGY

1. 2
2. 4
3. 4
4. 2
5. 1
6. 5
7. 5
8. 5
9. 3
10. 2
11. 1
12. 4
13. 1

SERIAL REASONING

1. 2
2. 4
3. 1
4. 5
5. 5
6. 4

APPENDIX A

BUBBLE TEST FORM

Many errors are made on the NNAT®* exam because the students do not know how to fill out a bubble test form. Have your child practice filling in answers in the bubbles below.

Examples

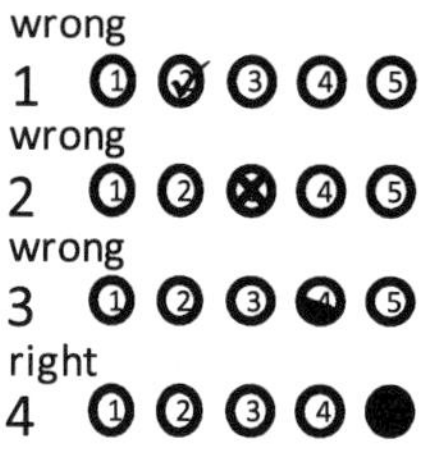

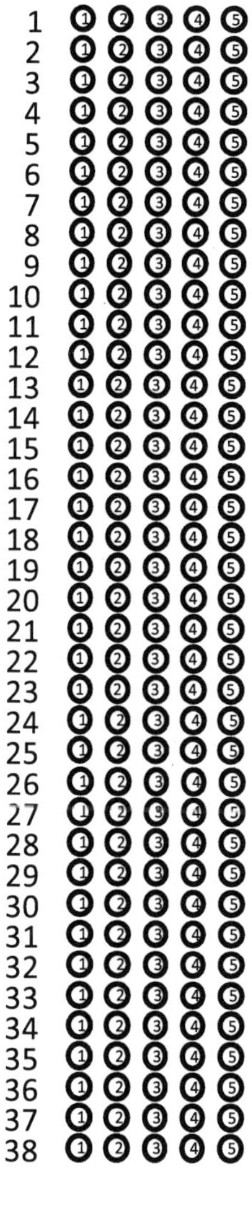

NOTES

NOTES

NOTES

NOTES

Mercer Publishing

Mercer Publishing understands how important it is to ensure your children are given the opportunities they deserve when it comes to their education. One of the greatest opportunities your child will have is entering the gifted program, if they can qualify for the program based on their test scores.

We provide practice test books for gifted program entry exams that offer:

- Similar questions and test formats to the actual tests
- Full length practice tests
- Answer keys

These books are invaluable tools for your child to score their best - and get into the gifted program!

Please visit our website to find out the current gifted program exams that are available.

WWW.MERCERPUBLISHING.COM